Skills Builders

Spelling and Vocabulary

YEAR
2

Brenda Stones

RISING ★ STARS

Rising Stars UK Ltd, 7 Hatchers Mews, Bermondsey Street, London SE1 3GS
www.risingstars-uk.com

Every effort has been made to trace copyright holders and obtain their permission for the use of copyright materials. The publishers will gladly receive information enabling them to rectify any error or omission in subsequent editions.

All facts are correct at time of going to press.

Published 2013
Text, design and layout © 2013 Rising Stars UK Ltd

Project manager and editorial: Dawn Booth
Proofreader: Claire Shewbridge
Design: Words & Pictures Ltd, London
Cover design: Amina Dudhia
Acknowledgements: p.6 i/Stock/Oscar Fernandez Chuyn; p.8 i/Stock/elvispupy; p.9, 10, 12, 17, 26, 27, 29, 35, 34, Dave Thompson; p.11 iStock/Govinda Jakosalem Trazo; p.12 i/Stock/Miroslaw Pieprzky; p.14 i/Stock/Alashi; p.16 i/Stock/Mark Stay; p.18 i/Stock/ryan burke; p.19 iStock/Mark Stay; p.28 i/Stock/konurk; p.32 i/Stock/Oscar Scottellaro; p.35 i/Stock/Julie Ridge; p.38 i/Stock/Mark Murphy; p.40 i/Stock/Dawn Hudson; p.46 *Oxford First Dictionary* (2011). Published by Oxford University Press

British Library Cataloguing-in-Publication Data
A CIP record for this book is available from the British Library.

ISBN: 978-0-85769-698-4
Printed in Singapore by Craft Print International

Skills Builders: Spelling and Vocabulary

YEAR
2

Contents

How to use this book

The content and sequence of this series of Skills Builders on Spelling and Vocabulary are closely based on the revised National Curriculum for English.

Provided within this book are:

1 Active teaching of individual spelling rules.

2 Emphasis on regular patterns in English spelling.

3 Writing grids to reinforce these spelling patterns.

4 Spelling jars and pots in which children make collections of common spellings.

5 Thematic vocabulary pages.

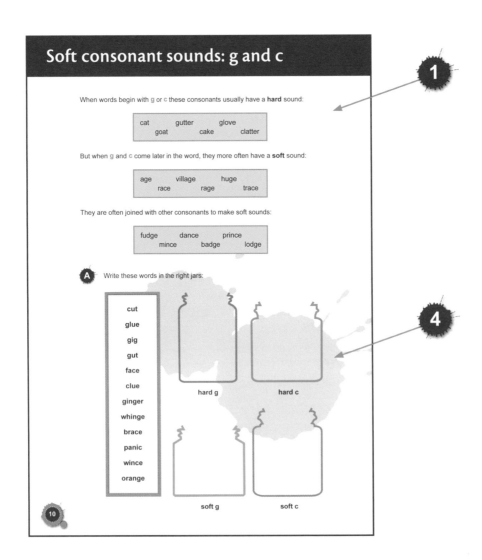

How to use this book

6 Occasional testing through dictation and word lists.

7 Three practical exercises that progress in difficulty.

8 Variety of layout, to help prepare for the new tests.

9 Encouragement of individual research in dictionaries and online.

10 Some more imaginative exercises on rhyme and alphabets.

11 'How did I do?' checks, for self-evaluation.

12 Answers are provided in a pull-out section for self-checking.

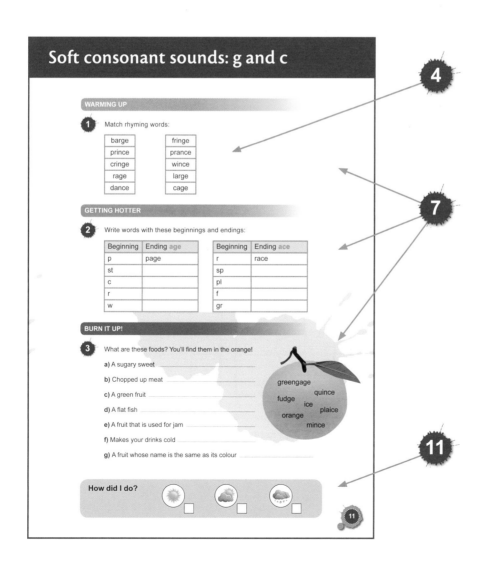

Soft consonant sounds: g and c

4

WARMING UP

1 Match rhyming words:

barge		fringe	
prince		prance	
cringe		wince	
rage		large	
dance		cage	

GETTING HOTTER

7

2 Write words with these beginnings and endings:

Beginning	Ending age
p	page
st	
c	
r	
w	

Beginning	Ending ace
r	race
sp	
pl	
f	
gr	

BURN IT UP!

3 What are these foods? You'll find them in the orange!

a) A sugary sweet _____

b) Chopped up meat _____

c) A green fruit _____

d) A flat fish _____

e) A fruit that is used for jam _____

f) Makes your drinks cold _____

g) A fruit whose name is the same as its colour _____

greengage
quince
fudge
ice
plaice
orange
mince

11

How did I do?

11

Phonics

A   Practise the five vowel sounds by filling in words that follow the spelling patterns.

i) Write words with a single consonant at the beginning:

m	mud		b	bed		l	lid		p	pot		c	cat
b			r			b			c			m	
c			l			h			r			h	
d			f			d			h			p	

ii) Write words with double consonants at the beginning:

br	brag		fl	fled		tr	trim		bl	blot		cl	club
cr			bl			br			pl			bl	
dr			cr			sl			cl			st	
fl			Fr			gr			tr			gr	

iii) Fill in words with double consonants at the end:

h	hang		b	bent		h	hint		b	bold		b	bust
b			r			t			c			m	
f			l			l			f			r	
r			d			m			h			d	

All these words have **short vowel** sounds, from just one vowel.

Phonics

WARMING UP

1 Match pairs of words that go together to make new words.

sing
dust
wind
cat
sun
lap

pan
top
set
mill
song
flap

GETTING HOTTER

2 Write these words in ABC order:

trip, flip, fling, ring, cling, thing, bring, clip, drip, grip

....

....

BURN IT UP!

3 Write rhyming words at the end of these lines:

One for a stamp,

Two for a ....

Three for a fling,

Four for a ....

Five for a thrill,

Six for a ....

Seven for a trend,

Eight for a ....

Nine for a song,

Ten for a ....

How did I do?

 ☐   ☐   ☐

Vowel digraphs

A Collect more words to add to each spelling pattern:

ai	rain
ay	day
ar	barn
aw	raw
ee	feel
ea	heat
er	fern
ew	threw
ie	pie
ir	fir
oa	boat
oe	toe
oi	boil
oo	moon
ou	shout
ow	cow
or	corn
ue	blue
ur	hurt

Vowel digraphs

WARMING UP

1 Copy these words to the right pot:

beat rain tie hurt pain clown steal burn lie frown

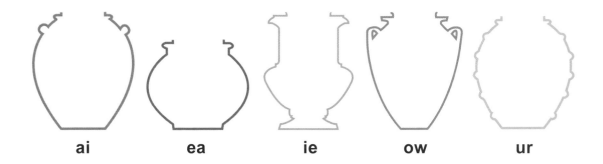

ai   ea   ie   ow   ur

GETTING HOTTER

2 Pair up words with the same sound, but different spellings:

been	fur
heal	bean
beat	blue
fir	beet
blew	heel

BURN IT UP!

3 Write three more rhyming words for each line:

a) pain: ....

b) harm: ....

c) feet: ....

d) corn: ....

e) flew: ....

How did I do?

 ☐   ☐   ☐

Soft consonant sounds: g and c

When words begin with **g** or **c** these consonants usually have a **hard** sound:

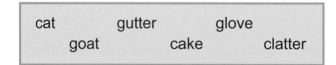

| cat | gutter | glove |
| goat | cake | clatter |

But when **g** and **c** come later in the word, they more often have a **soft** sound:

| age | village | huge |
| race | rage | trace |

They are often joined with other consonants to make soft sounds:

| fudge | dance | prince |
| mince | badge | lodge |

A   Write these words in the right jars:

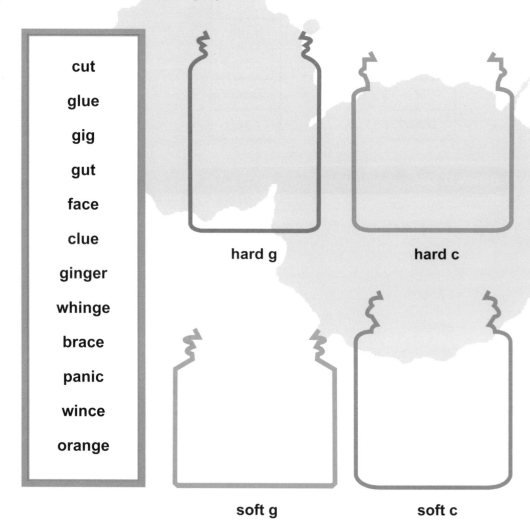

cut
glue
gig
gut
face
clue
ginger
whinge
brace
panic
wince
orange

hard g

hard c

soft g

soft c

Soft consonant sounds: g and c

1 Match rhyming words:

barge	fringe
prince	prance
cringe	wince
rage	large
dance	cage

2 Write words with these beginnings and endings:

Beginning	Ending age
p	page
st	
c	
r	
w	

Beginning	Ending ace
r	race
sp	
pl	
f	
gr	

3 What are these foods? You'll find them in the orange!

a) A sugary sweet _____

b) Chopped up meat _____

c) A green fruit _____

d) A flat fish _____

e) A fruit that is used for jam _____

f) Makes your drinks cold _____

g) A fruit whose name is the same as its colour _____

greengage
quince
fudge
ice
plaice
orange
mince

How did I do?

 ☐ ☐ ☐

11

Silent letters: k, g, w

We have many spellings that come from old English.

They have left us with some silent letters at the front of words:

> k in kn: knit, knot, know, knee, knife
>
> g in gn: gnome, gnat, gnaw
>
> w in wr: write, wrong, wrap, wreck

 A   Write these words in the right groups:

knew   wren   gnarled   knickers

knives   knock

wring

gnash   knots   kneel   wrist   wrote

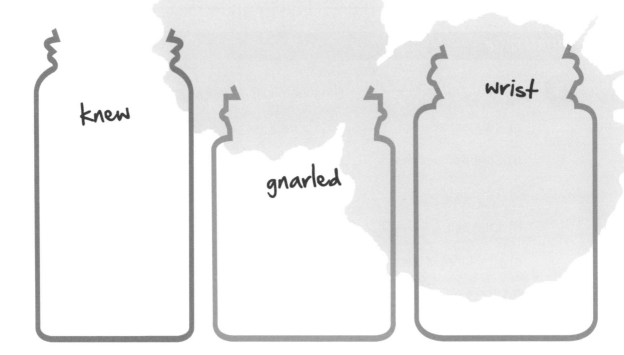

knew

gnarled

wrist

Silent letters: k, g, w

 1   Ring the word that belongs with the first word:

write:	wrote	worth	white	whose
knife:	kneel	knives	king	kind
gnash:	gnat	gate	gnashing	gash

 2   Write the words with these meanings. They are all on the opposite page.

a) A small bird ....

b) You cut with them ....

c) Between your hand and arm ....

d) It sits in the garden ....

e) Halfway up your leg ....

f) Not right ....

 3   Fill in words to complete the sentences:

a) I kn __ __ when I am right.

b) I wr __ __ __ with a pen.

c) I hate these flying gn __ __ __ .

d) I kn __ __ __ on the door.

e) I'll tie a kn __ __ to remember.

f) It's not right, it's wr __ __ __ .

How did I do?

 ☐   ☐   ☐

Magic e and endings

It's called magic e because it changes the middle vowel sound from short to long.

 A Add e to make new words, and say the two words to hear the difference.

bit	+ e =	bite
hat	+ e =	
fin	+ e =	
hug	+ e =	
not	+ e =	
cub	+ e =	
cut	+ e =	

shin	+ e =	
spin	+ e =	
spit	+ e =	
strip	+ e =	
trip	+ e =	
twin	+ e =	
cloth	+ e =	

 B Add endings to magic e words. You take off the e and add the ending.

	ing	ed	y
flake	flaking	flaked	flaky
stone			
bone			
pose			
phone			
taste			
paste			

Magic e and endings

1 Match up rhyming words:

shine
pale
spite
late
pole

fate
stole
male
fine
bite

GETTING HOTTER

2 Who are the people who do these things?

a) mine _____ miner _____

b) taste _____

c) hike _____

d) bike _____

e) file _____

BURN IT UP!

3 Put the right ending on each of the words given:

a) I was **hiking** down the road.

b) I was (**bike**) _____ up the hill.

c) Yesterday I (**time**) _____ her in the race.

d) My shoes are very (**shine**) _____ .

e) I was (**bite**) _____ my lip.

f) Last time, I (**line**) _____ up for the race.

How did I do?

 ☐   ☐   ☐

Short vowel sounds and endings

If we take the phonic words from Phonics A i) and A ii) on page 6 and add endings, we have to change the spelling.

Those words all have short vowel sounds and end with a single consonant.

To keep the vowel sound short you have to double the last letter:

pat, patting	pet, petting	pit, pitting	pot, potting	put, putting

The first word is called the **root word**.

 A Add endings to these root words in the same way:

root	ing	er	y
bat	batting	batter	batty
bid			
pot			
slip			
chat			
fat			
pat			
run			
flap			
pop			

Short vowel sounds and endings

1 This time, write the root words without their ending:

fat	fatty		smile	smiling
	rotter			hiking
	patting			miner
	sitting			rosy
	potter			bony

GETTING HOTTER

2 Write these words in the right jars:

> swimming   tapping   fatty   potter   happy   winning
> cutter   runny   swimmer   trimming

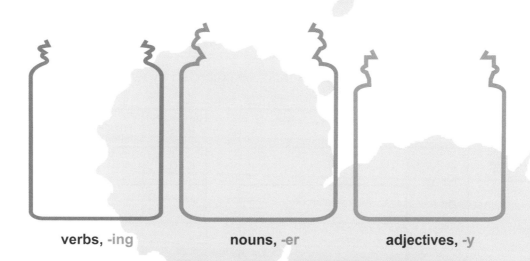

verbs, -ing   nouns, -er   adjectives, -y

BURN IT UP!

3 Write the right form of these words:

a) I was (**sit**) .... by the window.

b) I put a (**stop**) .... in the bottle.

c) I was (**ride**) .... my bike.

d) The honey is too (**run**) ....

e) I was (**let**) .... him go.

f) I find that very (**fun**) ....

How did I do?   ☐   ☐   ☐

Words ending -le

Words that end with **-le** follow the same rule as in "Magic e and endings" (page 14) and "Short vowel sounds and endings" (page 16).

If they have a **long vowel** sound, they are spelt with a single consonant.

If they have a **short vowel** sound, you double the consonant before adding **-le**.

 A   Practise both rules by listing these words:

t	table
f	
c	
g	
st	

b	babble
r	
d	
g	
scr	

B   The short vowel pattern is more common, so try two more vowel sounds:

d	diddle
f	
gr	
m	
r	

m	muddle
c	
f	
h	
p	

But there are some exceptions you just have to learn!

After double **n** or **r**, the ending is more often **-el**:
tunnel, funnel, quarrel, squirrel.

And the **ssle** sound is more often spelt **-istle**:
thistle, bristle, whistle, castle.

Words ending -le

 1

a) Make pairs of rhymes. Choose from these words:

huddle   throttle   nettle   muzzle   staple   dabble   haggle   thistle

bottle	
maple	
cuddle	
kettle	

gaggle	
guzzle	
whistle	
babble	

b) Can you think of more for each?

GETTING HOTTER

 2   Write these words in ABC order:

dribble, struggle, wobble, whistle, stable, funnel, paddle, barrel, juggle, cuddle

....

....

BURN IT UP!

 3   Match these words to their meanings:

cuddle
puzzle
bubble
thistle
struggle
cattle
gable

a game
air in water
cows
lots of hugs
a pointed roof
a prickly plant
a fight

How did I do?   ☐   ☐   ☐

Other vowel sounds

Here are some less common vowel sounds to learn:

Spelling	Sound	Sample words
a	or	tall, ball, walk, talk
ar	or	war, warm, reward
a	o	want, wash, watch
ea	ay	break, steak, great
ind	ynd	find, mind, kind
o	u	other, mother, brother
or	ur	word, work, worm
oor	or	floor, door, poor
ould	ood	could, would, should
u	oo	push, pull

A Collect more words that follow these patterns.

Other vowel sounds

WARMING UP

1 Match words that sound the same:

break		wood	
great		fined	
poor		grate	
find		brake	
would		pour	

GETTING HOTTER

2 Match words that rhyme:

warm		cake	
door		fate	
break		form	
kind		wood	
great		more	
tall		font	
word		fined	
want		wool	
pull		bird	
could		crawl	

BURN IT UP!

3 Choose the right spellings:

a) I will _____ you out of the _____ . (**pool / pull**)

b) My _____ is twice the age of my _____ . (**muther / mother; brother / bruther**)

c) I _____ you have been _____ . (**fined / find; kined / kind**)

d) Why don't you _____ me _____ my socks. (**wotch / watch; wosh / wash**)

e) The _____ is getting _____ . (**warld / world; wormer / warmer**)

f) If you _____ hard, you win _____ . (**work / wark; rewords / rewards**)

How did I do?

 ☐   ☐   ☐

Vocabulary: around the home

A **i)** In the bedroom, name the

bed

chair

carpet

table

books

pillow

window

clothes

ii) Add more labels of your own.

B **i)** In the kitchen, name the

cooker

sink

shelf

plates

cup

table

tap

fridge

ii) Add more labels of your own.

Answers

Skills Builders

Spelling and Vocabulary

YEAR
2

Brenda Stones

Phonics (pages 6–7)

A i) bud, cud, dud; red, led, fed; bid, hid, did;
cot, rot, hot; mat, hat, pat

ii) crag, drag, flag; bled, cred, Fred;
brim, slim, grim; plot, clot, trot; blub, stub, grub

iii) bang, fang, rang, rent, lent, dent, tint, lint,
mint, cold, fold, hold, must, rust, dust

1

sing	pan
dust	top
wind	set
cat	mill
sun	song
lap	flap

2 bring, cling, clip, drip, fling, flip, grip, ring, thing, trip

3 Answers will vary
Two for a lamp; Four for a sting; Six for a mill;
Eight for a bend; Ten for a wrong

Vowel digraphs (pages 8–9)

A Words will vary
pail, mail, jail; pay, say, ray; farm, darn, warn;
paw, saw, law; reel, heel, keel; meat, seat,
meal; tern, aero, berth, camper; new, ewe,
brew; lie, tie, die; sir, sire, mire; cloak, moat,
stoat; doe, foe, hoe; soil, toil, coil; soon, loose,
loot; mouse, doubt, lout; row, low, mow; born,
morn, torn; sue, due, rue; hurry, blur, during

1 ai: rain, pain; ea: beat, steal; ie: lie, tie; ow:
clown, frown; ur: hurt, burn

2 been, bean; heal, heel; beat, beet; fir, fur; blew, blue

3 Answers will vary
a) mane, sane, Jane **b)** arm, realm, alarm; farm
c) eat, seat, meat; **d)** lawn, sawn, worn
e) drew, mew, sew

Soft consonant sounds: g and c (pages 10–11)

A hard g: gut, gig, glue; hard c: cut, clue, panic;
soft g: orange, ginger, whinge; soft c: brace,
wince, face

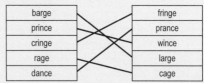

barge	fringe
prince	prance
cringe	wince
rage	large
dance	cage

2

Beginning	Ending age
st	stage
c	cage
r	rage
w	wage

Beginning	Ending ace
sp	space
pl	place
f	face
gr	grace

3. a) fudge **b)** mince **c)** greengage **d)** plaice
e) quince **f)** ice **g)** orange

Silent letters: k, g, w (pages 12–13)

A knew, knots, knives, knock, knickers, kneel;
gnarled, gnash; wrist, wring, wren, wrote

1 write: ⟨wrote⟩; knife: ⟨knives⟩; gnash: ⟨gnashing⟩

2 a) wren **b)** knives **c)** wrist **d)** gnome **e)** knee
f) wrong

3 a) know **b)** write **c)** gnats **d)** knock **e)** knot
f) wrong

Magic e and endings (pages 14–15)

A

hat	+ e =	hate
fin	+ e =	fine
hug	+ e =	huge
not	+ e =	note
cub	+ e =	cube
cut	+ e =	cute

shin	+ e =	shine
spin	+ e =	spine
spit	+ e =	spite
strip	+ e =	stripe
trip	+ e =	tripe
twin	+ e =	twine
cloth	+ e =	clothe

B

	ing	ed	y
stone	stoning	stoned	stony
bone	boning	boned	bony
pose	posing	posed	posy
phone	phoning	phoned	phony
taste	tasting	tasted	tasty
paste	pasting	pasted	pasty

1

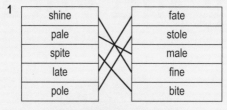

shine	fate
pale	stole
spite	male
late	fine
pole	bite

2 b) taster **c)** hiker **d)** biker **e)** filer
3 b) biking **c)** timed **d)** shiny **e)** biting **f)** lined

Short vowel sounds and endings (pages 16–17)

A.

root	ing	er	y
bid	bidding	bidder	biddy
pot	potting	potter	potty
slip	slipping	slipper	slippy
chat	chatting	chatter	chatty
fat	fatting	fatter	fatty
pat	patting	patter	patty
run	running	runner	runny
flap	flapping	flapper	flappy
pop	popping	popper	poppy

1

rot	rotter
pat	patting
sit	sitting
pot	potter

hike	hiking
mine	miner
rose	rosy
bone	bony

2 *verbs,* -ing: swimming, trimming, winning,
tapping; *nouns,* -er: potter, swimmer, cutter;
adjectives, -y: runny, fatty, happy

3 a) sitting **b)** stopper **c)** riding **d)** runny
e) letting **f)** funny

Words ending -le (pages 18–19)

A

f	fable
c	cable
g	gable
st	stable

r	rabble
d	dabble
g	gabble
scr	scrabble

B

d	diddle
f	fiddle
gr	griddle
m	middle
r	riddle

m	muddle
c	cuddle
f	fuddle
h	huddle
p	puddle

1 a) and **b)** Answers will vary

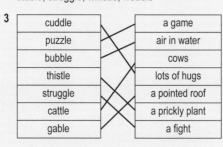

bottle	a) throttle b) shuttle
maple	a) staple b) ample
cuddle	a) huddle b) muddle
kettle	a) nettle b) settle

gaggle	a) haggle b) juggle
guzzle	a) muzzle b) drizzle
whistle	a) thistle b) castle
babble	a) dabble b) rabble

2 barrel, cuddle, dribble, funnel, juggle, paddle,
stable, struggle, whistle, wobble

3

cuddle	a game
puzzle	air in water
bubble	cows
thistle	lots of hugs
struggle	a pointed roof
cattle	a prickly plant
gable	a fight

Other vowel sounds (pages 20–21)

A Words will vary

Spelling	Sound	Sample words
a	or	gall, fall, stall
ar	or	wart, warn, ward
a	o	swatch, walk, ward
ea	ay	breakfast, greatest
ind	ynd	bind, binding, rind
o	u	smother, grandmother, motherhood
or	ur	worker, worse, worsen
oor	or	moor, doorknob, boor
ould	ood	wouldst, would-be
u	oo	pulling, pushing, pudding

1

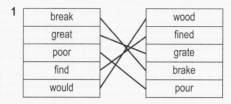

break	wood
great	fined
poor	grate
find	brake
would	pour

2

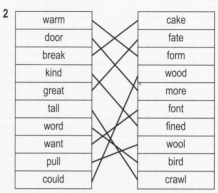

warm	cake
door	fate
break	form
kind	wood
great	more
tall	font
word	fined
want	wool
pull	bird
could	crawl

3 **a)** pull, pool **b)** mother, brother **c)** find, kind
d) watch, wash **e)** world, warmer
f) work, rewards

Vocabulary: around the home (pages 22–23)

A ii) Answers will vary
teddy bear, picture, T-shirt, trousers, lamp

B ii) Answers will vary
jug, frying pan, pots, saucer

1

car	room
win	chair
mush	pet
arm	lace
neck	dow

2 **a)** kitchen **b)** bedroom **c)** bedroom
d) kitchen **e)** kitchen

3 Answers will vary
sofa, chair, mirror, carpet, television, docking
station, video, computer

Suffix -ful, -less (adjectives) (pages 24–25)

A i)

play	+ ful =	playful
care	+ ful =	careful
peace	+ ful =	peaceful
fear	+ ful =	fearful
harm	+ ful =	harmful
hate	+ ful =	hateful

ii)

mind	+ less =	mindless
hope	+ less =	hopeless
care	+ less =	careless
fear	+ less =	fearless
harm	+ less =	harmless
love	+ less =	loveless

1

-ful	-less
careful	careless
fearful	fearless
harmful	harmless
hopeful	hopeless
joyful	joyless
mindful	mindless

2 **a)** hopeful **b)** careless **c)** powerful
d) fearless **e)** joyful

3 **a)**

hand	+ ful =	handful
cup	+ ful =	cupful
spoon	+ ful =	spoonful
plate	+ ful =	plateful
dish	+ ful =	dishful

b) Answers will vary
Harry said he had a handful of marbles but it
was really a cupful.

Suffix -er, -est (adjectives) (pages 26–27)

A

moist	moister	moistest
short	shorter	shortest
bold	bolder	boldest
pale	paler	palest
stale	staler	stalest

B

flat	flatter	flattest
thin	thinner	thinnest
slim	slimmer	slimmest
trim	trimmer	trimmest
glib	glibber	glibbest

1 **a)** later **b)** flattest **c)** fitter **d)** coldest
2

thick	thicker	thickest
thin	thinner	thinnest
hot	hotter	hottest
nice	nicer	nicest
white	whiter	whitest

3 **a)** hotter, hottest **b)** fatter, fattest **c)** nicer, nicest
d) warmer, warmest

Suffix -ing, -ed (verbs) (pages 28–29)

A

cool	cooling	cooled
mine	mining	mined
flip	flipping	flipped
stop	stopping	stopped
cram	cramming	crammed
chat	chatting	chatted
crawl	crawling	crawled
hum	humming	hummed
file	filing	filed
pipe	piping	piped
milk	milking	milked
rot	rotting	rotted

1 long vowel sound: shining, filing, pasted,
coasted; short vowel sound: lifted, misted,
humming, tugging

2

mating	matting
fusing	fussing
pined	pinned
fated	fatted
bated	batted

3 **a)** pinning **b)** fussed **c)** stripped **d)** filling
e) dining **f)** matting

Suffix -ness, -ment (nouns) (pages 30–31)

A

sad	+ ness =	sadness
fond	+ ness =	fondness
bold	+ ness =	boldness
joyful	+ ness =	joyfulness
plain	+ ness =	plainness

B

agree	+ ment =	agreement
disagree	+ ment =	disagreement
judge	+ ment =	judgement
disappoint	+ ment =	disappointment
fulfil	+ ment =	fulfilment

C

sister	+ hood =	sisterhood
child	+ hood =	childhood
neighbour	+ hood =	neighbourhood
knight	+ hood =	knighthood

member	+ ship =	membership
fellow	+ ship =	fellowship
head	+ ship =	headship
king	+ ship =	kingship

1 **a)** truthfulness **b)** girlhood **c)** professorship
  d) enjoyment **e)** ruthlessness **f)** judgement
2 family: brotherhood, motherhood, girlhood;
  other people: lordship, kingship, headship
3 **a)** judgement **b)** kindness **c)** boyhood
  d) sadness

Words ending in y (pages 32–33)

A

	-ed	-es	-ing
spy	spied	spies	spying
busy	busied	busies	busying
rely	relied	relies	relying
try	tried	tries	trying
fry	fried	fries	frying
carry	carried	carries	carrying
copy	copied	copies	copying
ferry	ferried	ferries	ferrying
marry	married	marries	marrying
tally	tallied	tallies	tallying

1

lady	ladies
hippy	hippies
copy	copies
jelly	jellies
monkey	monkeys
buggy	buggies
lorry	lorries

2

busy	business
waxy	waxiness
shiny	shininess
tufty	tuftiness
ready	readiness

3 **a)** trying **b)** tried **c)** cried **d)** lying **e)** flies
  f) relying

Vocabulary: out and about (pages 34–35)

A **ii)** Answers will vary
    trainers, spokes, helmet, backpack, hair
B **ii)** Answers will vary
    window, pram, mother, man, invalid, bag,
    aeroplane, zebra crossing, child

1

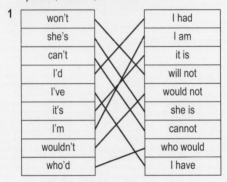

pave	box
bus	rail
hand	ment
match	door
trap	stop

2 2 wheels: bicycle; 3 wheels: penny farthing,
  tricycle; 4 wheels: bus, van, wheelchair
3 Answers will vary
  shop, shop window, street lamp, rubbish bin,
  lamppost

Apostrophes: missing letters (pages 36–37)

A **i)** o, o, o **ii)** a, a, a **iii)** i, i, i **iv)** a, ha, ha
  v) sha, wi, wi

B **i)** she's, who's, it's **ii)** we're, they're, you're
  iii) I'd, they'd, we'd **iv)** we'll, she'll, it'll
  v) aren't, couldn't, wouldn't

1

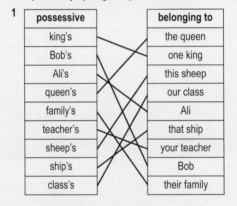

won't	I had
she's	I am
can't	it is
I'd	will not
I've	would not
it's	she is
I'm	cannot
wouldn't	who would
who'd	I have

2 **a)** shall not **b)** It is **c)** Who is **d)** must not
  e) sister is **f)** man has
3 **a)** mustn't **b)** wasn't **c)** Who's **d)** It's **e)** Can't
  f) shouldn't

Apostrophes: possessive (pages 38–39)

A **ii)** My aunt's books **iii)** The queen's crown
  iv) That sheep's tail **v)** The ship's cargo
  vi) Ravi's pen **vii)** Our class's vote
  viii) Our family's meal

B **i)** the doctor **ii)** that doctor **iii)** your family
  iv) her baby **v)** Megan **vi)** our class

1

possessive	belonging to
king's	the queen
Bob's	one king
Ali's	this sheep
queen's	our class
family's	Ali
teacher's	that ship
sheep's	your teacher
ship's	Bob
class's	their family

2 **a)** family's **b)** donkey's **c)** class's **d)** aunty's
  e) buggies' or buggy's **f)** tomato's
3 **a)** my cousin's book **b)** My father's shoes
  c) Our family's flat **d)** sheep's tail
  e) our class's notes **f)** sun's rays

Homophones (pages 40–41)

A **a)** see, sea **b)** for, four **c)** hear, here
  d) blew, blue **e)** bear, bare **f)** been, bean
  g) would, wood
  h) It's, its **i)** two, to, too **j)** they're, their, there

1

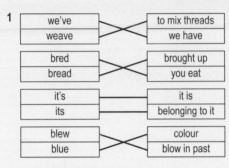

we've	to mix threads
weave	we have
bred	brought up
bread	you eat
it's	it is
its	belonging to it
blew	colour
blue	blow in past

2 **a)** past **b)** tied **c)** find **d)** ours **e)** break
3 **a)** tied, tide **b)** won, one **c)** flower, flour
  d) find, fined **e)** hoarse, horse

Using a dictionary (page 43)

1

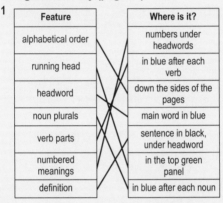

Feature	Where is it?
alphabetical order	numbers under headwords
running head	in blue after each verb
headword	down the sides of the pages
noun plurals	main word in blue
verb parts	sentence in black, under headword
numbered meanings	in the top green panel
definition	in blue after each noun

2

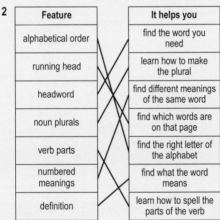

Feature	It helps you
alphabetical order	find the word you need
running head	learn how to make the plural
headword	find different meanings of the same word
noun plurals	find which words are on that page
verb parts	find the right letter of the alphabet
numbered meanings	find what the word means
definition	learn how to spell the parts of the verb

3 **a)** afraid
  b) after afraid
  c) ages
  d) Answers will vary
    The age of someone or something is how
    old they are.

Spelling test (page 44)

Great, owls, over, down, barrel or bucket, yellow,
eggs, thistle, hopping, inside, sitting, isn't, saddle,
toes, hammer, elbow, ears, nine, dinosaur.
Answer: Goodbye, this is the end!

Vocabulary: around the home

WARMING UP

1 Match these syllables to make words:

car
win
mush
arm
neck

room
chair
pet
lace
dow

GETTING HOTTER

2 In which room do you find these things?

a) dishwasher: _____

b) pillow: _____

c) blanket: _____

d) fridge: _____

e) microwave oven: _____

BURN IT UP!

3 What can you name in your living room?

_____

_____

_____

How did I do? ☐ ☐ ☐

Suffix -ful, -less (adjectives)

When you add an ending to a word, it is called a **suffix**.

hope + **ful** = **hopeful**, meaning full of hope

hope + **less** = **hopeless**, meaning without hope

These two suffixes start with consonants, so you don't need to change the spelling.

 i) Take nouns and add **-ful** to make adjectives:

joy	+ ful =	joyful
play	+ ful =	
care	+ ful =	
peace	+ ful =	
fear	+ ful =	
harm	+ ful =	
hate	+ ful =	

Note that **-ful** only has one l, even though it means "full of".

ii) Take nouns and add **-less** to make adjectives:

joy	+ less =	joyless
mind	+ less =	
hope	+ less =	
care	+ less =	
fear	+ less =	
harm	+ less =	
love	+ less =	

Suffix -ful, -less (adjectives)

 1 Which six words from the last page can end in **-ful** or **-less**?

-ful

-less

 2 Write adjectives with the suffix **-ful** or **-less** in the gaps:

a) We felt (**full of hope**) .... about going on holiday.

b) We were (**no care**) .... about packing the car.

c) The wind was (**full of power**) .... as we set out.

d) We felt (**no fear**) .... about the journey.

e) We felt (**full of joy**) .... when we arrived.

 3 Some words that end in **-ful** are nouns.

a) Complete the grid. They are all words that describe amounts of things

hand	+ ful =	handful
cup	+ ful =	
spoon	+ ful =	
plate	+ ful =	
dish	+ ful =	

b) Write a sentence using two of these nouns. ....

....

How did I do?

 ☐   ☐   ☐

25

Suffix -er, -est (adjectives)

We add the suffix **-er** and **-est** to adjectives when we want to compare them:

cold	col**der** meaning more cold	cold**est** meaning the most cold

These are called **comparative** adjectives.

 A The root word stays the same if:

- the short vowel sound is followed by two consonants, such as **thick**, **thicker**, **thickest**
- there is a long vowel sound, so **cool**, **cooler**, **coolest**
- if the adjective ends in **e**, you don't double the **e**, so **fine**, **finer**, **finest**.

Write these comparative adjectives:

black	blacker	blackest
moist		
short		
bold		
pale		
stale		

B You do change the spelling if the root word has a short vowel sound and ends with a single consonant. (See "Short vowel sounds and endings", page 16.)

With these words, double the last letter and add the ending:

fit	fitter	fittest
flat		
thin		
slim		
trim		
glib		

26

Suffix -er, -est (adjectives)

 1 Ring the odd one out:

a) hotter, fatter, later, thinner, flatter

b) pinkest, boldest, dampest, flattest

c) nicer, wiser, fitter, finer, later

d) thinnest, trimmest, coldest, fittest

 2 Add suffixes to these adjectives:

kind	kinder	kindest
thick		
thin		
hot		
nice		
white		

 3 Write **-er** and **-est** adjectives in the gaps:

a) Yesterday was hot, today is _____ , and tomorrow will be _____ .

b) He is fat, she is _____ , and he is _____ of all.

c) I am nice, he is _____ , and she is _____ of all.

d) This pool is warm, that one is _____ , and that one is the _____ .

How did I do?

Suffix -ing, -ed (verbs)

With verbs, we can add the suffixes **-ing** and **-ed**:

I am looking, she was looking, he looked.

I am tripping, she was tripping, he tripped.

Complete these, following the same spelling rules as in "Suffix **-er**, **-est** (adjectives)" on page 26:

- take off the final **e**; and double the last single consonant after a short vowel sound
- or double the last single consonant after a short vowel sound.

jump	jumping	jumped
cool		
mine		
flip		
stop		
cram		
chat		
crawl		
hum		
file		
pipe		
milk		
rot		

Suffix -ing, -ed (verbs)

1 Write these words in the right pots:

> shining   humming   filing   lifted   tugging
> misted   pasted   coasted

long vowel sound

short vowel sound

GETTING HOTTER

2 Write matching words with short vowel sounds and spellings:

filing	filling
mating	
fusing	
pined	
fated	
bated	

BURN IT UP!

3 Write the right word in the gaps:

a) I was (pining / pinning) _____ up the poster.

b) I got (fused / fussed) _____ about our lunch.

c) She had (striped / stripped) _____ off her clothes.

d) I was (filing / filling) _____ the bucket.

e) We eat in the (dining / dinning) _____ room.

f) Our floor is covered with (mating / matting) _____ .

How did I do?

29

Suffix -ness, -ment (nouns)

If you add the suffix **-ness**, **-ment**, **-hood** or **-ship**, you can make **abstract nouns**, which are nouns of ideas or feelings.

A Take adjectives and add **-ness**:

kind	+ ness =	kindness
sad	+ ness =	
fond	+ ness =	
bold	+ ness =	
joyful	+ ness =	
plain	+ ness =	

B Take verbs and add **-ment**:

enjoy	+ ment =	enjoyment
agree	+ ment =	
disagree	+ ment =	
judge	+ ment =	
disappoint	+ ment =	
fulfil	+ ment =	

C Take nouns and add **-hood** or **-ship**:

boy	+ hood =	boyhood		friend	+ ship =	friendship
sister	+ hood =			member	+ ship =	
child	+ hood =			fellow	+ ship =	
neighbour	+ hood =			head	+ ship =	
knight	+ hood =			king	+ ship =	

All these suffixes start with consonants, so you don't need to change the spelling.

Suffix -ness, -ment (nouns)

1 Match these root words with a suffix, and write the words on the lines:

truthful	ment
girl	ness
professor	ment
enjoy	ness
ruthless	ship
judge	hood

a) ....

b) ....

c) ....

d) ....

e) ....

f) ....

2 Write these words in the right jars:

kingship

motherhood

girlhood

headship

brotherhood

lordship

family   **other people**

3 Add the right suffix and write these words in the sentences:

a) You have shown good (judge) ....

b) Thank you for your (kind) ....

c) I remember that from my (boy) ....

d) We all felt great (sad) ....

How did I do?

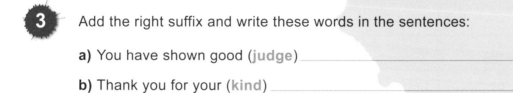

Words ending in y

When you add suffixes to words ending in **y**, it usually changes to **i**:

- **cry cried**
- **reply replied**
- **happy happiness**

- **busy busier busiest**
- **baby babies**

But when you add **-ing**, you leave the **y**:

- **cry crying**
- **rely relying**
- **reply replying**

 Add suffixes to these words:

	-ed	-es	-ing
cry	cried	cries	crying
spy			
busy			
rely			
try			
fry			
carry			
copy			
ferry			
marry			
tally			

Verbs that end in **-ie** also need a **y** before the **-ing** ending:

lie	lied	lies	lying
tie	tied	ties	tying

But words that have another vowel before the final **y** keep their spelling:

- **play played player**
- **enjoy enjoyed enjoys**

- **donkey donkeys**
- **key keyed**

Words ending in y

1 Make these plurals:

baby	babies
lady	
hippy	
copy	

jelly	
monkey	
buggy	
lorry	

GETTING HOTTER

2 Add **–ness** to make these adjectives into nouns:

happy	happiness
busy	
waxy	
shiny	
tufty	
ready	

BURN IT UP!

3 Write the right spellings:

a) I was (**try**) .... to spell this word.

b) I (**try**) .... several times.

c) I (**cry**) .... with the effort.

d) I was (**lie**) .... on the floor.

e) There are more (**fly**) .... in this room.

f) I am (**rely**) .... on you.

How did I do?

 ☐   ☐   ☐

Vocabulary: out and about

A   **i)**   On the bicycle, name the

saddle

wheel

pedal

brakes

bell

chain

lamp

handlebars

pump

ii)   Add more labels of your own.

B   **i)**   In the street, name the

shoppers, lorry, crossing, gutter, baby, buggy, bus, car, pavement, wheelchair

ii)   Add more labels of your own.

Vocabulary: out and about

1 Match these syllables to make words:

| pave |
| bus |
| hand |
| match |
| trap |

| box |
| rail |
| ment |
| door |
| stop |

2 How many wheels do these have? Copy the words into the right wheel:

tricycle   bus   van   bicycle   wheelchair   penny farthing

2 wheels   **3 wheels**   **4 wheels**

3 What else can you name in a street?

....

....

....

....

How did I do?

 ☐   ☐   ☐

Apostrophes: missing letters

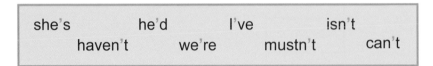

When people are speaking or writing fast, they start missing out letters.

When you write down these shortened words, you mark the missing letters with **apostrophes**:

she's	he'd	I've	isn't
haven't	we're	mustn't	can't

These are called **contractions**: they contract two words into one word, and miss out letters.

A Write which letters have been missed out in the following:

i) isn't _____ haven't _____ mustn't _____

ii) we're _____ you're _____ they're _____

iii) it's _____ she's _____ who's _____

iv) I'm _____ I'd _____ we'd _____

v) I'll _____ we'll _____ it'll _____

B Now write shortened versions of these words:

i) she is _____ who is _____ it is _____

ii) we are _____ they are _____ you are _____

iii) I had _____ they had _____ we would _____

iv) we shall _____ she will _____ it will _____

v) are not _____ could not _____ would not _____

Sometimes the contractions change the letters as well:

- **shall not, shan't**
- **will not, won't**

Apostrophes: missing letters

1 Match these contractions with the full words:

won't
she's
can't
I'd
I've
it's
I'm
wouldn't
who'd

I had
I am
it is
will not
would not
she is
cannot
who would
I have

2 Write full versions of these contractions:

a) I (**shan't**) _____ say what I think.

b) (**It's**) _____ raining again.

c) (**Who's**) _____ late again?

d) She (**mustn't**) _____ come in.

e) My (**sister's**) _____ on her way now.

f) That (**man's**) _____ not been there all week.

3 Write the contracted words in these sentences:

a) I (**must not**) _____ go there.

b) She (**was not**) _____ on the bus.

c) (**Who has**) _____ lost their purse?

d) (**It is**) _____ just not fair.

e) (**Cannot**) _____ we go a bit faster?

f) He (**should not**) _____ be here.

How did I do?

37

Apostrophes: possessive

The apostrophe has a second use: to show **possession**, as in **the girl's hair, the boy's toe**.

This use also started as a contraction: **the kinges crown** became the **king's crown**.

It doesn't matter how many objects the person owns: if it's a single owner, the apostrophe goes before the **s**.

 Turn these into possessives:

i) The pen of my aunt   *My aunt's pen*

ii) The books of my aunt

iii) The crown of the queen

iv) The tail of that sheep

v) The cargo of the ship

vi) The pen of Ravi

vii) The vote of our class

viii) The meal of our family

B Who do these things belong to?

i) The doctor's chair

ii) That doctor's chairs

iii) Your family's house

iv) Her baby's bottle

v) Megan's book

vi) Our class's notes

Apostrophes: possessive

 1 Match the words in the columns; so **king's** means belonging to **one king**.

Possessive
king's
Bob's
Ali's
queen's
family's
teacher's
sheep's
ship's
class's

Belonging to
the queen
one king
this sheep
our class
Ali
that ship
your teacher
Bob
their family

GETTING HOTTER

2 Correct these errors:

a) The familie's home

b) The donkeys' tail

c) The clas'ss books

d) My auntys' scarf

e) The buggys' wheels

f) Your tomatoe's leaves

BURN IT UP!

3 Write the possessive forms in these sentences:

a) I lost (**the book of my cousin**) .

b) (**The shoes of my father**) are black.

c) (**The flat of our family**) is home.

d) The (**tail of the sheep**) was fluffy.

e) I found (**the notes of our class**) .

f) Where are the (**rays of the sun**) ?

How did I do?   ☐   ☐   ☐

Homophones

Homophones are words that sound the same but are spelled differently:

> hear, here
>
> there, their, they're
>
> weave, we've
>
> wood, would

They always have different meanings, so the spelling has to be right.

 A Fill in the right words in these sentences.

a) We can _____ the _____ . (**sea / see**)

b) I waited _____ you for _____ minutes. (**for / four**)

c) I can _____ you from _____ . (**here / hear**)

d) You _____ out the _____ candle. (**blue / blew**)

e) I can't _____ running in _____ feet. (**bear / bare**)

f) I have _____ known to eat a green _____ . (**bean / been**)

g) They _____ prefer it to be made of _____ . (**wood / would**)

h) _____ sitting on _____ tail. (**its / it's**)

i) I've got _____ minutes _____ decide if I'll come _____ . (**two / too / to**)

j) I know _____ thinking about leaving _____

   shirts _____ . (**there / their / they're**)

Homophones

1 Match these homophones to their meaning:

we've	to mix threads	bred	you eat
weave	we have	bread	brought up

it's	it is	blew	colour
its	belonging to it	blue	blow in past

2 Write homophones for these words:

a) passed

b) tide

c) fined

d) hours

e) brake

3 Fill in the right words in these sentences:

a) I _____ up the boat before the _____ came in. (**tide / tied**)

b) She _____ the race in _____ minute. (**one / won**)

c) You sniffed the _____ and mixed the _____ .
(**flower / flour**)

d) We _____ we have been _____ for speeding.
(**fined / find**)

e) My voice is _____ as I ride this _____ .
(**horse / hoarse**)

How did I do?   ☐   ☐   ☐

41

Using a dictionary

Here is a page from the *Oxford First Dictionary*:

Aa

accident accidents
An accident is something nasty that was not meant to happen.

act acts, acting, acted
If you act, you pretend to be someone else in a play, show, or film.

add adds, adding, added
1 When you add something, you put it with something else.
2 When you add numbers, you work out how many you get when you put them together. So, three add two equals five.

$$3 + 2 = 5$$

address addresses
Your address is the number of your house, and the name of the street and town where you live.

AIR MAIL

The Queen,
Buckingham Palace,
Buckingham Palace Road,
London UK
SW1A 1AA

adult adults
An adult is a person or animal that has grown up.

adventure adventures
An adventure is something exciting that happens to you.

aeroplane aeroplanes
An aeroplane is a flying machine with wings, and usually one or more engines.

afraid
Someone who is afraid thinks something bad might happen to them.

4

Using a dictionary

1 Find and match each feature from the dictionary page:

Feature
alphabetical order
running head
headword
noun plurals
verb parts
numbered meanings
definition

Where is it?
numbers under headwords
in blue after each verb
down the sides of the pages
main word in blue
sentence in black, under headword
in the top green panel
in blue after each noun

GETTING HOTTER

2 What do these features help you do? Match the correct answers:

Feature	
alphabetical order	
running head	
headword	
noun plurals	
verb parts	
numbered meanings	
definition	

It helps you
find the word you need
learn how to make the plural
find different meanings of the same word
find which words are on that page
find the right letter of the alphabet
find what the word means
learn how to spell the parts of the verb

BURN IT UP!

3 Answer these questions based on the dictionary page opposite:

a) Which word is an adjective? _____

b) Where would you add the word "age"? _____

c) What would you add after the headword for "age"? _____

d) What would you write as a definition for "age"? _____

_____

How did I do?

 ☐   ☐   ☐

Spelling test

Write the words, starting with the first letter in the yellow column.

— — — — — Britain								
night birds								
opposite of under								
opposite of up								
you keep water in it								
colour of the sun								
hens lay them								
comma sign								
prickly plant								
add -ing to hop								
opposite of outside								
add -ing to sit								
contraction of is not								
seat of a bicycle								
five of them on your foot								
you hit nails with it								
halfway up your arm								
you hear with them								
one less than ten								
Tyrannosaurus Rex								

!

Reading down the yellow column says:

PIANO
VOCAL
GUITAR

SELENA GOMEZ & The...
WHEN THE SUN GOES DOWN

© Disney Enterprises, Inc.

ISBN 978-1-4584-1617-9

SEVEN PEAKS MUSIC

DISTRIBUTED BY

Hal•Leonard
CORPORATION

7777 W. Bluemound Rd. P.O. Box 13819 Milwaukee, WI 53213

Visit Hal Leonard Online at
www.halleonard.com

LOVE YOU LIKE A LOVE SONG

option 1: Am, C, G, D

Words and Music by TIM JAMES,
ANTONINA ARMATO and ADAM SCHMALHOLZ

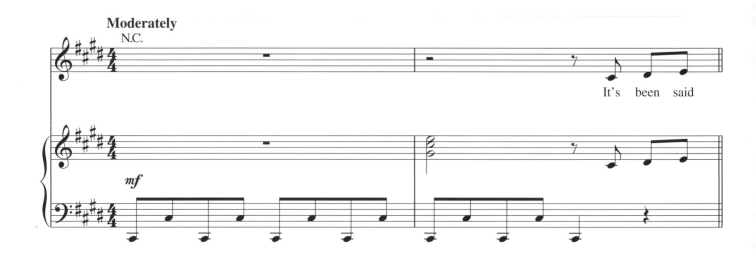

It's been said

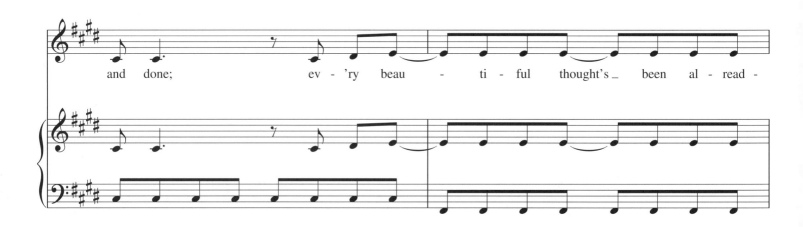

and done; ev - 'ry beau - ti - ful thought's __ been al - read -

y sung, and I guess __ right now __ here's an - oth - er one, so your mel -

BANG BANG BANG

Words and Music by TOBY GAD,
MELENI SMITH and PRISCILLA RENEA

WHO SAYS

Words and Music by PRISCILLA RENEA
and EMANUEL KIRIAKOU

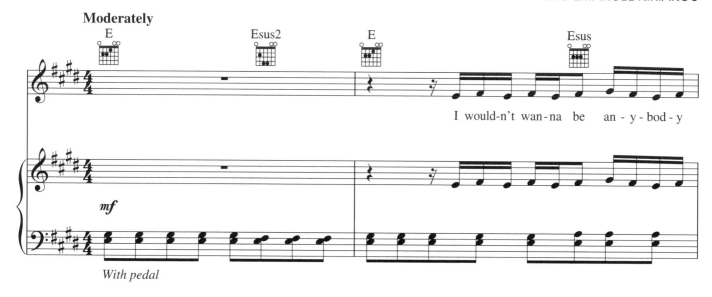

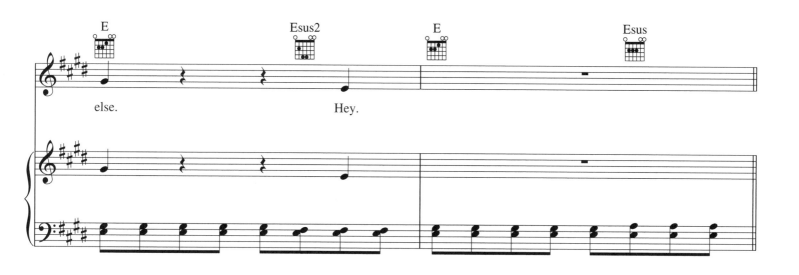

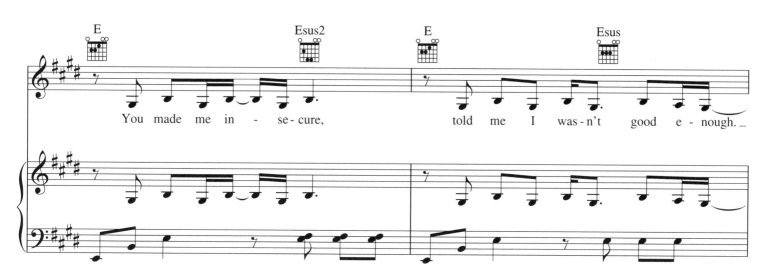

18

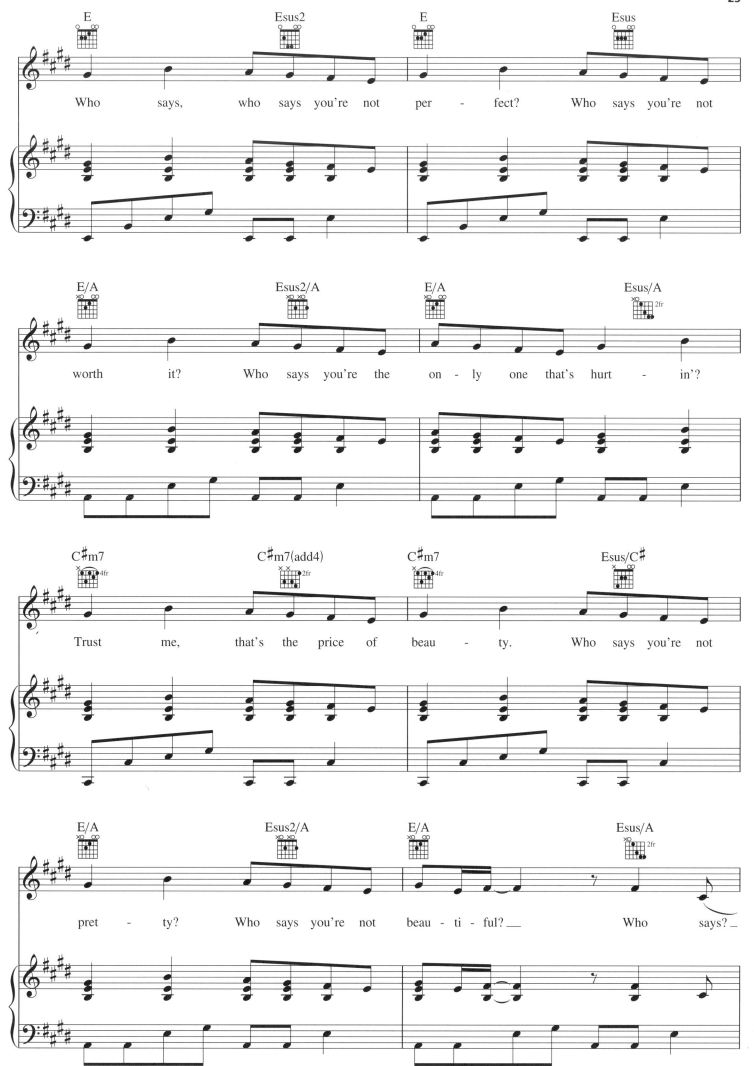

WE OWN THE NIGHT

Words and Music by TOBY GAD
and VICTORIA LOTT

option 1: verse: Em, G, Em, G / Am, D7, G, Em / G, Am, C, Em / C, Am, G, Em | chorus: Em, G, G, D7 / Em, G, C, Am

HIT THE LIGHTS

Words and Music by LEAH HAYWOOD,
DANIEL JAMES and TONY NILSSON

Dance beat
Em7
Gsus2/C
It's the boy you nev - er told, "I like you." It's the
time that you to - tal - ly screwed up; still you're
mf
With pedal
G
Gmaj7
Bm/F♯
Em7
girl you let get a - way. It's the one you saw that day
try'n' to get it out your brain. It's the fight you had when you did -
Gsus2/C
G
Gmaj9/F♯
on a train, but you freaked out and walked a - way. It's the
- n't make up. It's the past that your dy - in' to change. It's

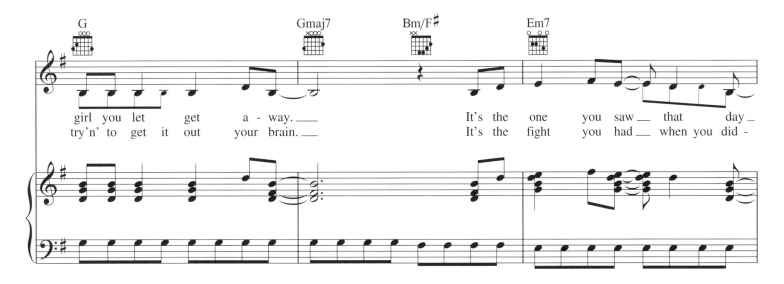

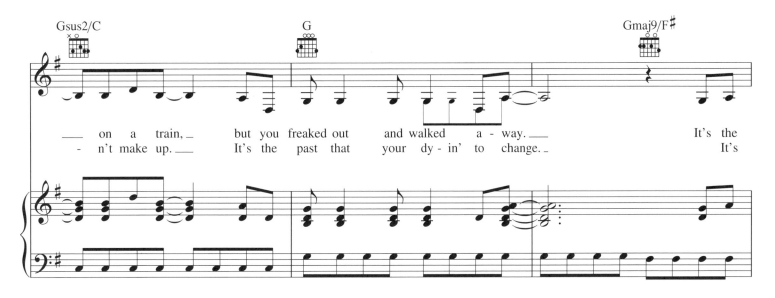

WHIPLASH

Words and Music by BRITNEY SPEARS,
GREGORY KURSTIN and NICOLE MORIER

WHEN THE SUN GOES DOWN

Words and Music by SELENA GOMEZ,
JOEY CLEMENT, STEVE SULIKOWSKI
and STEFAN ABINGDON

Moderate Dance beat

With pedal

Been a long day; _ wait-ing for the night to come. _

I check my i - Phone; _

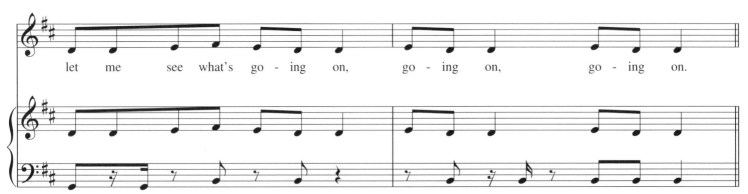

let me see what's go-ing on, go-ing on, go-ing on.

* *Recorded a half step lower.*

MY DILEMMA

Words and Music by TIMOTHY PRICE,
ANTONINA ARMATO and DEVRIM KARAOGLU

THAT'S MORE LIKE IT

Words and Music by KATY PERRY,
BILLY STEINBERG and JOSH ALEXANDER

When I wanted you, ___
When my birth-day came, ___

you would not re-cip-ro-cate. ___ When I
you would not re-mem-ber it. ___ When I

need-ed you, ___ you would al-ways show up late. ___ But
talked to you, ___ you were nev-er lis-ten-ing. ___ But

Whoa, ___ right ___ now. ___

That's ___ more ___ like ___ it; ___ yeah,

D.S. al Coda

Bm7

CODA

Em7

N.C.

option: G, C, Em

OUTLAW

Words and Music by SELENA GOMEZ,
TIMOTHY PRICE, ANTONINA ARMATO
and THOMAS ARMATO STURGES

Recorded a half step lower.

Oh. ____ I'm gon-na seal your fate, make you pay for all ____ of your sins. Oh, ____ uh oh.

You've been rid - ing this horse ____ a long time; ____ I've had my eye on you ____ all night. ____ I'm gon-na find a way to

MIDDLE OF NOWHERE

Words and Music by ESPEN LIND,
AMUND BJORKLUND, SANDY WILHELM
and CARMEN MICHELLE KEY

Lyrics:

You left me spin - ning like a
You left me brok - en like a

dis - co, try - ing but I don't know if I can
rec - ord, ba - by, I'm, ba - by, I'm ___ hurt and I don't

stand straight. ___
wan - na play ___ an - y - more. ___

You took me, left, when you knew
Missed ev - 'ry sign, be -